Puzzles to Puzzle You

- Discover adventure and excitement of mathematical puzzles!
- Match your wits with the human computer!!
- Sharpen your intellect, delight your friends and enjoy hours of purposeful entertainment!!!

Mathematics is not always hard, mind-boggling stuff. It can also be simple, interesting and delightful. Many famous mathematicians are known to be devoted to peg jumping puzzles. It is perhaps this kind of play that leads on to scientific discoveries.

The celebrity author, Shakuntla Devi, is regarded as an 'authentic heroine of the twentieth century' She calculates faster than the fastest computer, is listed in the Guinness Book of Records and continues to amaze audiences around the world with her feats of calculation.

By the same author
in
Orient Paperbacks

Mathability: The Math Genius in Your Child
Figuring: The Joy of Numbers
Puzzles to Puzzle You
More Puzzles to Puzzle You
The Book of Numbers
Astrology for You
Perfect Murder
Awaken the Genius in Your Child

PUZZLES TO PUZZLE YOU

Shakuntala Devi

Orient Paperbacks

DELHI | MUMBAI | HYDERABAD

ISBN : 978-81-222-0014-0

Puzzles To Puzzle You

Subject: Games / Puzzles

© Shakuntala Devi

1st Published 1976
44th Printing 2013

Published by
Orient Paperbacks
(A division of Vision Books Pvt. Ltd.)
5A/8 Ansari Road, New Delhi-110 002
www.orientpaperbacks.com

Cover design by Vision Studio

Printed at
Anand Sons, Delhi-110 092, India

Cover Printed at
Ravindra Printing Press, Delhi-110 006, India

PREFACE

What is mathematics? It is only a systematic effort of solving puzzles posed by nature.

Recreational mathematics, in a way, is pure mathematics and it is often difficult to distinguish pure mathematics from recreational mathematics. However, it may also be considered applied mathematics in the sense it satisfies the human need for intellectual play. And solving wits and puzzles, in a way, helps to develop wit and ingenuity.

The pedagogic value of recreational mathematics is now widely recognised and creative mathematicians are never embarrassed to show their interest in recreational topics. Today one finds an increasing emphasis on it in journals published for mathematical instructors and in modern text books.

It is said that the famous mathematician Leibnitz spent considerable time to the study of peg-jumping puzzles. And is also a well known fact that Prof. Albert Einstein's bookshelf was stacked with books on mathematical games and puzzles. It is creative thoughts bestowed on such mathematical play, that has led many a great mind to scientific discoveries.

While solving of the mathematical puzzles and riddles may provide pleasant relaxation to some, undoubtedly these items have a way of hooking the students' interest as little else can.

Some of the puzzles I am posing in the following pages show very elegant facts and proofs in mathematics. Many who consider the subject dull and boring will see that some facts of mathematics can be quite simple, interesting and even beautiful. These are not riddles made to deceive, or nonsensical puzzles which are made to tease the mind without purpose. The puzzles included in this book are straightforward exercises in reason and statement of facts from which a person with reasonably agile mind can proceed to a logical conclusion.

I have no doubt my readers will find adventure, excitement, and delight in cracking the clean, sharply defined, and mysterious order that underlay the puzzles, and experience enormous intellectual entertainment.

Shakuntala Devi

Puzzles

*Amusement is one of the fields of
applied mathematics.*
W.F. White

1
Tall Men Next Door

Next door to me live four brothers of different heights. Their average height is 74 inches, and the difference in height amongst the first three men is two inches. The difference between the third and the fourth man is six inches.

Can you tell how tall is each brother?

2
A Matter of Time

Fifty minutes ago if it was four times as many minutes past three o'clock, how many minutes is it to six o'clock?

3

Brothers and Sisters

A family I know has several children. Each boy in this family has as many sisters as brothers but each girl has twice as many brothers as sisters.

How many brothers and sisters are there?

4

Around the Equator

T wo identical trains, at the equator start travelling round the world in opposite directions. They start together, run at the same speed and are on different tracks.

Which train will wear out its wheel treads first?

Over the Golden Gate

While in San Francisco some time back, I hired a car to drive over the Golden Gate bridge. I started in the afternoon when there was no traffic rush. So I could drive at a speed of 40 miles an hour. While returning, however, I got caught in the traffic rush and I could only manage to drive at a speed of 25 miles an hour.

What was my average speed for the round trip?

The Digits and Square Numbers

All the nine digits are arranged here so as to form four square numbers:

9,   81,   324,   576

How would you put them together so as to form a single smallest possible square number and a single largest possible square number?

Bicycle Thieves

A friend of mine runs a bicycle shop and he narrated to me this following story:

A man, who looked like a tourist, came to his shop one day and bought a bicycle from him for Rs. 350. The cost price of the bicycle was Rs. 300. So my friend was happy that he had made a profit of Rs. 50 on the sale. However, at the time of settling the bill, the tourist offered to pay in travellers cheques as he had no cash money with him. My friend hesitated. He had no arrangement with the banks to encash travellers cheques. But he remembered that the shopkeeper next door has such a provision, and so he took the cheques to his friend next door and got cash from him.

The travellers cheques were all of Rs. 100 each and so he had taken four cheques from the tourist totalling to Rs. 400. On encashing them my friend paid back the tourist the balance of Rs. 50

The tourist happily climbed the bicycle and pedalled away whistling a tune.

However, the next morning my friend's neighbour, who had taken the travellers cheques to the bank, called on him and returned the cheques which had proved valueless and demanded the refund of his money. My friend quietly refunded the money to his neighbour and tried to trace the tourist who had given him the worthless cheques and taken away his bicycle. But the tourist could not be found.

How much did my friend lose altogether in this unfortunate transaction?

The Bus Number

While visiting a small town in the United States, I lost my overcoat in a bus. When I reported the matter to the bus company I was asked the number of the bus. Though I did not remember the exact number I did remember that the bus number had a certain peculiarity about it. The number plate showed the bus number was a perfect square and also if the plate was turned upside down, the number would still be a perfect square—of course it was not?

I came to know from the bus company they had only five hundred buses numbered from 1 to 500.

From this I was able to deduce the bus number.

Can you tell what was the number?

The Hour Hand and the Minute Hand

We all know that the hour hand and the minute hand on a clock travel at different speeds. However, there are certain occasions when they are exactly opposite each other. Can you give a simple formula for calculating the times of these occasions?

To Catch a Thief

Some time back while in England I came across a case in a criminal court. A man was being accused of having stolen certain valuable jewels and trying to run away with them, when he was caught by a smart police officer who overtook him.

In cross examination the lawyer for accused asked the police officer how he could catch up with the accused who was already twenty seven steps ahead of him, when he started to run after him. 'Yes sir,' the officer replied. 'He takes eight steps to every five of mine.'

'But then officer', interrogated the lawyer, 'how did you ever catch him, if that was the case?'

'That's easily explained sir,' replied the officer, 'I have got a longer stride... two steps of mine are equal to his five. So the number of steps I required were fewer than his, and this brought me to the spot where I captured him.'

A member of the jury, who was particularly good at quick calculations did some checking and figured out the number of steps the police officer must have taken.

Can you also find out how many steps the officer needed to catch up with the thief?

11
The Gong

Supposing a clock takes 7 seconds to strike 7, how long will the same clock take to strike 10?

12
Something for the Marmalade

A little girl I know sells oranges from door to door.

One day while on her rounds she sold $1/2$ an orange more than half her oranges to the first customer. To the second customer she sold $1/2$ an orange more than half of the remainder and to the third and the last customer she sold $1/2$ an orange more than half she now had, leaving her none.

Can you tell the number of oranges she originally had? Oh, by the way, she never had to cut an orange.

The Counterfeit Note

While walking down the street, one morning, I found a hundred rupee note on the footpath. I picked it up, noted the number and took it home.

In the afternoon the plumber called on me to collect his bill. As I had no other money at home, I settled his account with the hundred rupee note I had found. Later I came to know that the plumber paid the note to his milkman to settle his monthly account, who paid it to his tailor for the garments he had made.

The tailor in turn used the money to buy an old sewing machine, from a woman who lives in my neighbourhood. This woman incidentally, had borrowed hundred rupees from me sometime back to buy a pressure cooker, remembering that she owed me hundred rupees, came and paid the debt.

I recognised the note as the one I had found on the footpath, and on careful examination I discovered that the bill was counterfeit.

How much was lost in the whole transaction and by whom?

14

Cotton or Gold

Which would you say is heavier, a pound of cotton or a pound of gold?

15

Nuts for the Nuts

Last time I visited a friend's farm near Bangalore he gave me a bag containing 1000 peanuts. From this I took out 230 peanuts for myself and gave away the bag with the remainder of peanuts to three little brothers who live in my neighbourhood and told them to distribute the nuts among themselves in proportion to their ages—which together amounted to $17^1/2$ years.

Tinku, Rinku and Jojo, the three brothers, divided the nuts in the following manner:

As often as Tinku took four Rinku took three and as often as Tinku took six Jojo took seven.

With this data can you find out what were the respective ages of the boys and how many nuts each got?

16
The Wedding Anniversary

Recently I attended the twelfth wedding anniversary celebrations of my good friends Mohini and Jayant. Beaming with pride Jayant looked at his wife and commented, 'At the time when we got married Mohini was $^3/_4$th of my age, but now she is only $^5/_6$th.'

We began to wonder how old the couple must have been at the time of their marriage!

Can you figure it out?

17
I'll Get it for You Wholesale...

A wholesale merchant came to me one day and posed this problem. Every day in his business he had to weigh amounts from one pound to one hundred and twenty-one pounds, to the nearest pound. To do this, what is the minimum number of weights he needs and how heavy should each weight be?

The Broken Glasses

My friend Asha was throwing a very grand party and wanted to borrow from me 100 wine glasses. I decided to send them through my boy servant, Harish.

Just to give an incentive to Harish to deliver the glasses intact I offered him 3 paise for every glass delivered safely and threatened to forefeit 9 paise for every glass he broke.

On settlement Harish received Rs. 2.40 from me. How many glasses did Harish break?

The Peculiar Number

There is a number which is very peculiar. This number is three times the sum of its digits. Can you find the number?

Make a Century

There are eleven different ways of writing 100 in the form of mixed numbers using all the nine digits once and only once. Ten of the ways have two figures in the integral part of the number, but the eleventh expression has only one figure there.

Can you find all the eleven expressions?

The Perplexed Postal Clerk

My friend Shuba works in a post office and she sells stamps. One day a man walked in and kept seventy five paise on the counter and requested, 'Please give me some 2 paise stamps, six times as many as one paisa stamps, and for the rest of the amount give me 5 paise stamps.'

The bewildered Shuba thought for a few moments and finally she handed over the exact fulfilment of the order to the man—with a smile.

How would you have handled the situation?

The Mystery of the Missing Paisa

Two women were selling marbles in the market place—one at three for a paisa and other at two for a paisa. One day both of them were obliged to return home when each had thirty marbles unsold. They put together the two lots of marbles and handing them over to a friend asked her to sell them at five for 2 paise. According to their calculation, after all, 3 for one paisa and 2 for one paisa was exactly the same as 5 for 2 paise.

Now they were expecting to get 25 paise for the marbles, as they would have got, if sold separately. But much to their surprise they got only 24 paise for the entire lot.

Now where did the one paisa go? Can you explain the mystery?

Walking back to Happiness

A man I know, who lives in my neighbourhood, travels to Chinsura everyday for his work. His wife drives him over to Howrah Station every morning and in the evening exactly at 6 p.m. She picks him up from the station and takes him home.

One day he was let off at work an hour earlier, and so he arrived at the Howrah Station at 5 p.m. instead of at 6 p.m. He started walking home. However, he met his wife enroute to the station and got into the car. They drove home arriving 10 minutes earlier than usual.

How long did the man have to walk, before he was picked up by his wife?

24
On the Line

It is a small town railway station and there are 25 stations on that line. At each of the 25 stations the passengers can get tickets for any of the other 24 stations.

How many different kinds of tickets do you think the booking clerk has to keep?

25
The Legacy

When my uncle in Madura died recently, he left a will, instructing his executors to divide his estate of Rs. 1,920,000 in this manner: Every son should receive three times as much as a daughter, and that every daughter should get twice as much as their mother.

What is my aunt's share?

The Round Table

We have a circular dining table made of marble which had come down to us as a family heirloom. We also have some beautiful bone-china saucers that I recently brought from Japan.

Diameter of our table top is fifteen times the diameter of our saucers which are also circular. We would like to place the saucers on the table so that they neither overlap each other nor the edge of the table.

How many can we place in this manner?

Down the Escalator

Recently while in London, I decided to walk down the escalator of a tube station. I did some quick calculation in my mind. I found that if I walk down twenty-six steps, I require thirty seconds to reach the bottom. However, if I am able to step down thirty-four stairs I would only require eighteen seconds to get to the bottom.

If the time is measured from the moment the top step begins to descend to the time I step off the last step at the bottom, can you tell the height of the stairway in steps?

The Chess Board

We all know that a chess board has 64 squares. This can be completely covered by 32 cardboard rectangles, each cardboard covering just 2 squares.

Supposing we remove 2 squares of the chess board at diagonally opposite corners, can we cover the modified board with 31 rectangles? If it can be done. how can we do it? And if it cannot be done, prove it impossible.

The Game of Cats and Mice

A number of cats got together and decided to kill between them 999919 mice. Every cat killed an equal number of mice.

How many cats do you think there were?

Oh, by the way let me clarify just two points—it is not one cat killed the lot, because I have said 'Cats' and it is not 999919 cats each killed one mouse, because I have used the word 'mice'

I can give you just one clue—each cat killed more mice than there were cats.

30
The Wheels

A friend of mine in Bangalore owns a horse-driven carriage. It was found that the fore wheels of the carriage make four more revolutions than the hind wheel in going 96 feet. However, it was also found that if the circumference of the fore wheel was $3/_2$ as great and of the hind wheel $4/3$ as great, then the fore wheel would make only 2 revolutions more than hind wheel in going the same distance of 96 feet.

Can you find the circumference of each wheel?

31
Blow Hot Blow Cold

It is a matter of common knowledge that 0°C is the same as 32°F. It is also a known fact that 100°C equals 212°F. But there is a temperature that gives the same reading on both Centigrade and Fahrenheit scales.

Can you find this temperature?

The Llama Race

Recently, while I was in a holiday resort in Peru I watched a very interesting spectacle. Two gentlemen by the name of Sr. Guittierez and Sr. Ibanez decided to have a Llama race over the mile course on the beach sands. They requested me and some of my other friends whom I had met at the resort to act as the judges. We stationed ourselves at different points on the course, which was marked off in quarter miles.

But, the two Llamas, being good friends decided not to part company, and ran together the whole way. However, we the judges, noted with interest the following results.

The Llamas ran the first three quarters in six and three quarters minutes. They took the same time to run the first half mile as the second half. And they ran the third quarter in exactly the same time as the last quarter.

From these results I became very much interested in finding out just how long it took those two Llamas to run the whole mile.

Can you find out the answer?

The Shattered Clock

A clock with the hours round the face in Roman block numbers, as illustrated in the sketch fell down and the dial broke into four parts. The numerals in each part in every case summed to a total of 20.

Can you show how the four parts of the clock face was broken?

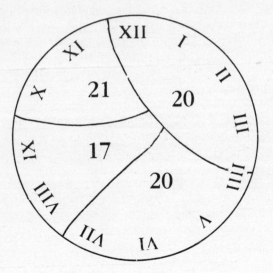

34

The Painted Window

My room has a square window of 4 feet across and 4 feet down. I decided to get only half the area of the window painted. Even after the painting I found that the clear part of the window still remained a square and still measured 4 feet from top to bottom and 4 feet from side to side.

How is it possible?

35

Animals on the Farm

My friend who owns a farm near Bangalore had five droves of animals on his farm consisting of cows, sheep and pigs with the same number of animals in each drove.

One day he decided to sell them all and sold them to eight dealers.

Each of the eight dealers bought the same number of animals and paid at the rate of Rs. 17 for each cow, Rs. 2 for each sheep and Rs. 2 for each pig.

My friend received from the dealers in total Rs. 285.

How many animals in all did he have and how many of each kind?

Which is the Better Bargain?

Recently while shopping in New Market in Calcutta, I came across two very nice frocks selling at a discount. I decided to buy one of them for my little girl Mammu. The shopkeeper offered me one of the frocks for Rs. 35 usually selling for $8/7$ of that price and the other one for Rs. 30 usually selling for $7/6$ of that price.

Of the two frocks which one do you think is a better bargain and by how much per cent?

Walking all the Way

One day I decided to walk all the way from Bangalore to Tumkur. I started exactly at noon. And someone I know in Tumkur decided to walk all the way to Bangalore from Tumkur and she started exactly at 2 P.M., on the same day.

We met on the Bangalore-Tumkur Road at five past four, and we both reached our destination at exactly the same time.

At what time did we both arrive?

The Train and the Cyclist

A railway track runs parallel to a road until a bend brings the road to a level crossing. A cyclist rides along to work along the road every day at a constant speed of 12 miles per hour.

He normally meets a train that travels in the same direction at the crossing.

One day he was late by 25 minutes and met the train 6 miles ahead of the level crossing. Can you figure out the speed of the train?

Something for Profit

A friend of mine bought a used pressure cooker for Rs. 60. She somehow did not find it useful and so when a friend of hers offered her Rs. 70 she sold it to her. However, she felt bad after selling it and decided to buy it back from her friend by offering her Rs. 80. After having bought it once again she felt that she did not really need the cooker. So she sold it at the auction for Rs. 90.

How much profit did she make? Did she at all make any profit?

40

The Digital Game

There is a number, the second digit of which is smaller than its first digit by 4, and if the number was divided by the digits'sum, the quotient would be 7.

Can you find the number?

41

The Faulty Machine

A factory manufacturing flywheels for racing cars has ten machines to make them. The manufacturer knows the correct weight for a flywheel.

However, one day one of the machine begins to produce faulty parts—either overweight or underweight.

How can the manufacturer find the faulty machine in only two weighings?

The Number and the Square

In the diagram the numbers from 1 to 9 are arranged in a square in such a way that the number in the second row is twice that in the first row and the number in the bottom row three times that in the top row.

I am told that there are three other ways of arranging the numbers so as to produce the same result.

Can you find the other three ways?

1	9	2
3	8	4
5	7	6

Squares and Right Angles

Can you make 2 squares and 4 right-angled triangles using only 8 straight lines?

The Dishonest Merchant

An unscrupulous trader decided to make some extra profit on coffee. He bought one type of coffee powder at Rs. 32 a kilo and mixed some of it with a better quality of coffee powder bought at Rs. 40 a kilo, and he sold the blend at Rs. 43 a kilo. That gave him a profit of 25 per cent on the cost.

How many kilos of each kind must he use to make a blend of a hundred kilos weight?

For the Charities

One day when I was walking on the road in New Delhi, a group of boys approached me for donation for their poor boys' fund. I gave them a rupee more than half the money I had in my purse. I must have walked a few more yards when a group of women approached me for donation, for an orphanage. I gave them two rupees more than half the money I had in my purse. Then, after a few yards I was approached by a religious group for a donation to the temple they were building. I gave them three rupees more than half of what I had in my purse.

At last when I returned to my hotel room, I found that I had only one rupee remaining in my purse.

How much money did I have in my purse when I started?

The Number Game

The product of three consecutive numbers when divided by each of them in turn, the sum of the three quotients will be 74.

What are the numbers?

47

The Sari and the Blouse

I bought a sari and a blouse for Rs. 110 at the New Market. The sari cost Rs. 100 more than the blouse, how much does the sari cost?

48

When was he Born?

Some months back, this year, I was walking through the Central Park in New York.

I saw an intelligent looking little boy playing all by himself on the grass. I decided to talk to him and just as an excuse to start the conversation I asked him his age. A mischievous glint flickered in his eyes and he replied, 'Two days back I was ten years old, and next year I shall be thirteen. If you know what's today, you'll be able to figure out my birthday and that'll give you my age.' I looked at him bewildered.

How old was the boy?

The Weight of the Block

A cement block balances evenly on the scales with three quarters of a pound and three quarters of a block. What is the weight of the whole block?

Lucrative Business

Two unemployed young men decided to start a business together. They pooled in their savings, which came to Rs. 2,000. They were both lucky, their business prospered and they were able to increase their capital by 50 per cent every three years.

How much did they have in all at the end of eighteen years.

The Old Ship

Some years back I was travelling by a cargo ship from New Zealand to Tahiti. I was curious to look around the ship one day, and in the boiler room I asked a man how old the ship was. He smiled and replied in this way: 'The ship is twice as old as its boiler was when the ship was as old as the boiler is now. And the combined age of the ship and the boiler is thirty years.'

Can you figure out what is the age of the ship and of the boiler?

The Three Containers

We have three containers which hold 19, 13 and 7 ounces of liquid respectively. The 19 ounce container is empty but the 13 and 7 ounces containers are full. How can we measure out 10 ounces by using only the three above mentioned containers?

53

On the Way to Market

One morning I was on my way to the market and met a man who had 4 wives. Each of the wives had 4 bags, containing 4 dogs and each dog had 4 puppies.

Taking all things into consideration, how many were going to the market?

54

A Matter of Denominator

A fraction has the denominator greater than its numerator by 6. But if you add 8 to the denominator, the value of the fraction would then become $\frac{1}{3}$.

Can you find this fraction?

55
Right Foot Forward

A short man takes three steps to a tall man's two steps. They both start out on the left foot. How many steps do they have to take before they are both stepping out on the right foot together?

56
A Problem of Socks

Mammu wears socks of two different colours – white and brown. She keeps them all in the same drawer in a state of complete disorder.

She has altogether 20 white socks and 20 brown socks in the drawer. Supposing she has to take out the socks in the dark, how many must she take out to be sure that she has a matching pair?

A Fair Division

A rich farmer died leaving behind a hundred acres of his farm to be divided among his three daughters Rashmi, Mala and Rekha—in the proportion of one-third, one-fourth and one-fifth, respectively. But Rekha died unexpectedly.

Now how should the executor divide the land between Rashmi and Mala in a fair manner?

Mathematics and Literature

Recently a publishing company which specialises in mathematical books, advertised the job opening of an assistant editor. The response was good. One hundred people applied for the position. The company, however, wanted to make their selection from the applicants who had some training in both mathematics and literature.

Out of one hundred applicants the company found that 10 of them had no training in mathematics and no training in literature, 70 of them had got mathematical training and 82 had got training in literature.

How many applicants had got training in both mathematics and literature?

Heads I Win Tails I Lose

During my last visit to Las Vegas in the U.S.A., I met a man who was an inveterate gambler. He took out a coin from his pocket and said to me, 'Heads I win, tails I lose. I'll bet half the money in my pocket.'

He tossed the coin, lost and gave me half the money in his pocket. He repeated the bet again and again each time offering half the money in his pocket.

The game went on for quite some time. I can't recollect exactly how long the game went on or how many times the coin was tossed, but I do remember that the number of times he lost was exactly equal to the number of times he won.

What do you think, did he, on the whole, gain or lose?

Problem from Lilavati

Here is an ancient problem from Bhaskaracharya's Lilavati:

A beautiful maiden, with beaming eyes, asks me which is the number that, multiplied by 3, then increased by three-fourths of the product, divided by 7, diminished by one-third of the quotient, multiplied by itself, diminished by 52, the square root found, addition of 8, division by 10 gives the number 2?

Well, it sounds complicated, doesn't it? No, not if you know how to go about it.

Up the Ladder

A man wants to reach a window which is 40ft. above the ground. The distance from the foot of the ladder to the wall is 9 feet.

How long should the ladder be?

Pigs and Ducks

While driving through the countryside one day I saw a farmer tending his pigs and ducks in his yard. I was curious to know how many of each he had. I stopped the car and inquired.

Leaning on the stile jovially, he replied, 'I have altogether 60 eyes and 86 feet between them'.

I drove off trying to calculate in my mind the exact number of ducks and pigs he had.

What do you think is the answer?

The Faulty Watch

One day I found a strange thing happening to my watch—the minute hand and the hour hand were coming together every sixty-five minutes. I decided to get it checked.

Was my watch gaining or losing time, and how much per hour?

The Egg Vendor and His Eggs

Rasool, the man who delivers eggs to my home everyday, did not turn up one day. So when he came the next morning I demanded an explanation from him. He told me the following story:

The previous morning when he just came out of the house carrying a basketful of eggs on his head to start his daily rounds and stepped on to the street, a car going at full speed brushed against him and knocked down his basket destroying all the eggs. The driver, however, a thorough gentleman admitted his responsibility and offered to compensate him for damages. But Rasool could not remember the exact number of eggs he had, but he estimated the number between 50 and 100. He was also able to tell the gentleman that if the eggs were counted by 2's and 3's at a time, none would be left, but if counted by 5's at a time, 3 would remain, and that he sold the eggs 50 paise a piece.

The gentleman made some quick calculations and paid Rasool adequately.

How much did the gentleman pay Rasool?

Some Luck!

A society of farmers who own farms in the vicinity of my home town Bangalore, planned on holding a raffle and persuaded me to buy a ticket. The value of the ticket was Rs. 5. As I did not want to pay the entire amount myself, I asked my friend Radha to chip in with me, and offered to share with her in proportion the prize bounty— if there was going to be any. She paid Rs. 2 and I paid the rest.

As luck would have it—Bingo! ... we won the first prize—a flock of 50 sheep! Good God! ... Neither of us knew what to do with the sheep ... Where would we take them in the first place? Neither of us had had any training as shepherds! So we decided to sell the sheep back to the farmers.

As per our original understanding 20 of the sheep belonged to Radha and 30 were mine.

However, I decided that we had won the prize because of our combined luck, and so we should divide its value equally.

The sheep-30 of mine and 20 of Radha's-were sold, each at the same price, and I paid her Rs. 150 to make the sum equal.

What was the value per sheep?

The Trains and the Falcon

Two trains start from two opposite directions towards each other. The stations from which they start are 50 miles apart. Both the trains start at the same time on a single track. A falcon which is sitting on one train, starts at the same time towards the other train, as soon as it reaches the second one, it flies back to the first train and so on and so forth. It continues to do so, flying backwards and forwards from one train to the other until the trains meet.

Both the trains travel at a speed of 25 miles per hour, and the bird flies at 100 miles per hour.

How many miles will the falcon have flown before the trains meet?

Which is more Lucrative?

A businessman advertised two job openings for peons in his firm. Two men applied and the businessman decided to engage both of them. He offered them a salary of Rs. 2,000 per year; Rs. 1,000 to be paid every half year, with a promise that their salary would be raised if their work proved satisfactory. They could have a raise of Rs. 300 per year, or if they preferred, Rs. 100 each half year.

The two men thought for a few moments and then one of them expressed his wish to take the raise at Rs. 300 per year, while the other man said he would accept the half yearly increase of Rs. 100.

Between the two men, who was the gainer, and by how much?

68

Little Mammu and the Marbles

Little Mammu was playing marbles with her friend Nawal I heard her say to him, 'if you give me one of your marbles I'll have as many as you.' Nawal replied, 'if you give me one of your marbles, and I'll have twice as many as you.'

I wondered how many marbles each had! What do you think?

69

A Family Matter

Fifteen years back my neighbour Mrs. Sareen had three daughters Sudha, Seema and Reema—and their combined ages were half of hers. During the next five years Sonny was born and Mrs. Sareen's age equalled the total of all her children's ages.

After some years Kishu was born and then Sudha was as old as Reema and Sonny together. And now, the combined age of all the children is double Mrs. Sareen's age, which is, as a matter of fact, only equal to that of Sudha and Seema together. Sudha's age is also equal to that of the two sons.

What is the age of each one of them?

The High-Rise

While in Canada, I visited a beautiful high-rise building in the Metropolitan City of Toronto. The manager of the building told me that the building consisted of different kinds of apartments large and small. Two room apartments were 5% in number, $2^1/_2$'s—7% in number, 3's—15% in number, $3^1/_2$'s—20% in number, $4^1/_2$'s—49% in number, 5's-33% in number, $5^1/_2$'s—12% in number, 6's—3% in number and in addition several 4 room apartments. Altogether the building contained 437 apartments.

Can you figure out how many apartments are there in each type, using round figures?

The Curious License Plate

When I acquired my Mercedes-Benz car in Germany, the first thing I had to do was to get a license plate. The plate I got had a peculiar number on it. It consisted of 5 different numbers and by mistake when I fixed it upside down the number could be still read, but the value had increased by 78633.

What was my actual license number?

72
Lose or Gain

A man I know runs a workshop in Calcutta. He bought two lathes to use in his workshop. However, he found out afterwards that they did not serve the purpose for which he had bought them, and so he decided to sell them. He sold them each for Rs. 600 making a loss of 20% on one of them and a profit of 20% on the other.

Did he lose or gain in the transaction, and how much did each machine cost him?

73
A Problem of Combination

A box contains 12 marbles of three different colours green, yellow and blue—4 each.

If you were to close your eyes and pick them at random, how many marbles must you take out to be sure that there are at least two of one colour among the marbles picked out?

On the See-Saw

Some days back, walking through the park, I saw a little girl trying to play the see-saw all by herself. It takes two to see-saw, but here was a girl who was ingenious enough to try and see-saw on her own.

I saw her tying a number of bricks to one end of the plank to balance her weight at the other.

I curiously noted that she just balanced against sixteen bricks, when these were fixed to the short end of the plank and I also noticed that if she were to fix them to the long end of the plank, she only needed eleven as balance.

I wondered what was the girl's weight. The brick. I could guess weighed equal to a three quarter brick and three quarter of a pound.

Can you figure it out?

75
The Special Number

There is a number whose double is greater than its half by 45.

Can you find this number?

76
Sawing the Tree Trunk

A heavy tree trunk can be sawed into a 12 ft long piece in oneminute. How long will it take to saw it into twelve equal pieces?

The Bigamist

A man I know in Bombay committed bigamy by marrying two women at brief intervals, one without the knowledge of the other. Somehow he was not brought to the notice of the law and though, if exposed the axe could fall on him any day, he decided to get the best out of the situation while it lasted.

He was fond of both the women and had no special preference for either. One lived near Churchgate and the other in Bandra. He worked near a station midway between Churchgate and Bandra.

After work he generally went to the station, and took that train which got into the station first–Churchgate or Bandra. He arrived at his destination at random timings, but found that he was visiting his Churchgate wife much more often than the other, despite the fact that both the Churchgate and Bandra trains were on schedules which brought him to his station equally often. The same thing had been happening for a very long time.

Can you find the reason for the frequency of his Churchgate trips?

The Split

Can you split 34 parts into two parts such that $4/7$ of one of the parts equals $2/5$ of the other?

At the Fete

A number of us went out together to a charity fete one day. Our party consisted of 4 different professional groups, namely 25 writers, 20 doctors, 18 dentists and 12 bank employees. We spent altogether Rs. 1,330

Later it was found that 5 writers spent as much as four doctors, that twelve doctors spent as much as nine dentists, and that six dentists spent as much as eight bank employees.

How much did each of the four professional groups spend?

At the Store

I entered a store and spent one-half of the money that was in my purse. When I came out I found that I had just as many paise as I had rupees and half as many rupees as I had paise when I went in.

How much money did I have, with me when I entered?

The Counterfeit Coins

During my last visit to the U.K. I spent a few days in a small town, where I stayed as a paying guest with a British landlady. The heaters in the rooming house were all coin operated.

One day my landlady requested my help in sorting out a problem.

There were one hundred and twenty coins in her gasmeter and one of them, she knew, was counterfeit. The counterfeit coin was either heavier or lighter than the others.

Now the problem was to isolate this coin and find out whether it was lighter or heavier, in five weighings.

How can one do it?

82
Multiplying Bacteria

Bacteria is known to multiply very rapidly.

A certain container contains just one bacteria on the first day and there are twice as many on the next day. In this manner the number of bacteria in the container doubles itself everyday.

Assuming that the container would be full of bacteria on the 10th day, on which day would the container be half full.

83
A Puzzling Number

There is a number which is greater than the aggregate of its third, tenth and the twelfth parts by 58.

Can you find the number?

What a Coincidence!

A group of seven young men named Arun, Binoy, Chunder, Dev, Edward, Fakruddin and Govind were recently engaged in a game. They had agreed that whenever a player won a game he should double the money of each of the other players, in other words he was to give the players just as much money as they had already in their pockets.

In all they played seven games and, strangely, each won a game in turn in the order in which their names are given. But what was even more strange was that when they had finished the game each of the seven young men had exactly the same amount, Rs. 32 in his pocket.

Can you find out how much money each person had with him before they began the game?

The Idler

Ram Rakhan was well known all around his neighbourhood for being a very lazy person. So when he went around looking for a job as a farm-hand everyone refused to engage him, except farmer Gulab Singh, who was a very smart person.

Gulab Singh engaged the services of Ram Rakhan at a salary of Rs. 240 a month consisting of 30 days. However, he set a condition that he would forefeit Rs. 10 for each day that he idled. Ram Rakhan accepted the job.

At the end of the month it was found that neither owed the other anything. This taught a lesson to Ram Rakhan.

Can you tell just how many days Ram Rakhan worked and how many days he idled?

Numbers Game

During one of my tours to Canada, I came across a very interesting game participated by two players.

A group of match sticks is placed on the table and then it is reduced in turn by each player by removing from the group at least 1 but not more than 4 match sticks.

The player who takes the last match stick is the winner.

If there is a group of 17 match sticks on the table how would you make your first move, if it was your turn and how would you continue to play to win?

A Bargain in Guavas

Recently I bought some guavas at New Market for Rs. 1.20. But they were so small that I made the vendor throw in two extra guavas for the same price.

As I began to walk away the vendor mumbled that this transaction had made him lose 10 paise a dozen less than the price settled before.

How many guavas did I get for my Rs. 1.20?

The Mathematical Shepherd

Shepherd Gopal had a curious aptitude for mathematics and he was known around where he lived as the 'Counting Shepherd'.

A man passing through the meadow one day saw Gopal grazing a number of sheep and in the course of a short conversation asked him how many of the grazing sheep were his own. Gopal's reply absolutely baffled him, which was as follows:

'If you divide my sheep into two different parts, the difference between the two numbers will be the same as the difference between their squares. Now figure it out for yourself the number of sheep I own.'

Can you say just how many sheep Gopal had?

Father and Son

A father, I know, is 4 times his son's age. And in 30 years son's age will be half of his father's age.

How old are the father and son now?

Shown in the sketch are six matchsticks.

Can you rearrange them to make nothing?

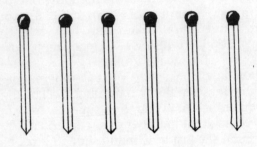

91
No Change Please!

I had Rs. 1.15 in my purse in 6 coins, but I found that I could not give change for a rupee, half a rupee, quarter rupee, ten paise or five paise.

Which 6 coins did I have?

92
A Date to Reckon With

The date 8.8.64, meaning August 8,1964 is a very interesting date, because the product of the first two numbers equals the third.

Can you find the year of the twentieth century which gives the maximum dates of this kind?

93
Gold for All Occasions

Which is worth more, a bucket full of half a sovereign gold pieces or an identical bucket full of 1 sovereign gold pieces?

94
The Ink-Spot

One day, Mammu set a very interesting problem to me. She pushed a large circular table we have at home, into the corner of the room, so that it touched both walls and spilled a spot of ink on the extreme edge, and she said, 'Mummy here is a little puzzle for you. Look at that spot. It is exactly eight inches from one wall and nine inches from the other. Now tell me the diameter of the table without measuring it........'

Can you?

Spade for a Heart

Here is a spade:

Can you cut the spade into three pieces that will fit together and form a heart?

Remember, no part of the material should be wasted.

The Number Puzzle

There are two numbers with the difference of 3 between them and the difference of their squares is 51. Can you find the numbers?

A Problem of Coins

Can you place 10 coins in such a way that they lie in 5 straight lines and on each line there are 4 coins. There are at least two solutions.

The Squirrel and the Post

I saw a squirrel climbing up a cylindrical post spirally, making the circuit in four feet.

Supposing the top of the post is sixteen feet high and three feet in circumference, how many feet does it travel to the top?

Hearts Apart

A man I know fell in love with a woman who lived 63 miles away. Finally he decided to propose marriage to his beloved and invited her to travel towards his place and offered to meet her enroute and bring her home.

The man is able to cover 4 miles per hour to the woman's 3 miles per hour.

How far will each have travelled upon meeting?

The Curfew

In most States in India the law for the sale of alcoholic beverages provides that beer cannot be sold after a certain hour. However, in some States the law permits a customer to consume, after the deadline, what has been sold before the curfew.

In a certain bar 2 men ordered sufficient beer to cover their probable requirements in anticipation of the curfew. One man ordered and paid for 5 bottles and the other man ordered and paid for 3 bottles. But as the curfew started, an old friend of both the men approached and requested them to share the eight bottles of beer between them.

The friend thanked the two men and put down Rs. 8 in payment for the beer he had consumed, asking them to share the money in proportion to the quantity of beer they have contributed to him.

How should this money be equitably divided between the two men?

101
A Problem of Age

Recently I met a woman I hadn't seen for a long time. In the course of conversation she said, 'Do you know something funny? If you reverse my own age, the figures represent my husband's age. He is, of course, senior to me and the difference between our age is one-eleventh of their sum.

Can you find out the woman's age as well as her husband's age?

102
The Passenger Train and the Goods Train

Two trains, a passenger train and a goods train, are running in the same direction on parallel railway tracks. The passenger train takes three times as long to pass the goods train—even when they are going in the opposite directions.

If the trains run at uniform speeds, how many times faster than the goods train is the passenger train moving?

The Circular Numbers

Here is a sketch:

Can you rearrange the position of the numbers 1 to 10 so that the sum of any two adjacent numbers is equal to the sum of the pair of numbers at the opposite ends of the diameters?

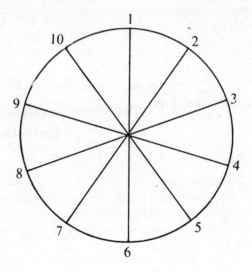

Rice for the Festival

At a certain festivity a rich man decided to distribute free rice to deserving people. He had altogether 100 kilos of rice and he wanted to distribute the grain to 100 people in such a manner that each old person received three kilos, each young person two and each child half a kilo. How many old persons, young persons and children were there?

Threes to Make Thirty-one

Can you write 31 using only digit 3 five times?

106
Swarm of Bees

Here is another problem from Bhaskaracharya's Lilavati:

The square root of half the number of bees in a swarm has flown out upon a jasmine bush; eight ninths of the whole swarm has remained behind; one female bee flies about a male that is buzzing within the lotus flower into which he was allured in the night by its sweet odour, but is now imprisoned in it. Tell me the number of bees?

107
Story of the Three Farmers

Three farmers paid Rs. 1,000 for a small pasture. One farmer grazed his 9 mules, another his 12 cows for twice the time and last man put in some goats for $2\frac{1}{2}$ times as the second man's cows and paid half the cost of the pasture.

Can you find out how many goats did the last man have, if 6 cows eat as much as 4 mules, and 10 goats as much as 3 cows? And how much did the first and second man each pay?

What Were You Doing When the Lights Went Out?

Last time there was load shedding in Calcutta, I was reading a very interesting book and I could not stop. My neighbour Parveen gave me two candles and assured me that I could manage with them.

Though the candles were of the same length, Parveen told me that one candle would burn for four hours and the other for five hours.

After I had been reading for some time I put the candles out as the lights came on again. And I noticed that what remained of one candle was exactly four times the length of what was left of other.

Can you find out just how long those two candles were burning?

Staff and the Steeple

A five feet long staff casts a shadow 2 feet long. Can you find the height of a steeple whose shadow at the same hour, is 120 ft. long?

The Dotted Square

Twenty-five dots are arranged in a square formation in 5 rows of 5, as shown in the sketch:

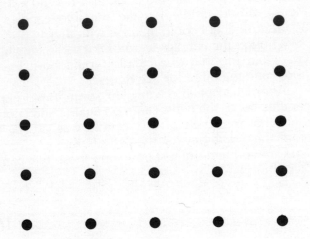

Can you connect 12 of these dots with straight lines to form a perfect cross which has five dots inside it and 8 dots outside?.

111
Up the Stream—Down the Stream

While up stream, a crew can row a boat in eight and four-sevenths minutes. But if there was no stream they could row it in seven minutes less than it takes them to drift down the stream.

Can you say how long it would take them to row down with the stream?

112
Wine and Water

While I was talking to a chemist one day, he set me this interesting problem:

'I decided to mix some wine spirits and water. I had two bottles containing 10 ounces of each. I poured just a quarter of an ounce of spirits into the water and shook them up. You can see clearly that the mixture was forty to one. Now I thought that I should have the same quantity of fluid in both the bottles, and so I poured back a quarter of an ounce of the mixture into the bottle containing spirits.'

Can you tell what proportion of spirits to water did the spirits of wine bottle then contain?

113
The Long Tunnel

A train is one mile long. It travels at the rate of one mile a minute through a tunnel which is also one mile long.

Can you say how long it will take for the train to pass completely through the tunnel?

114
The Horse, the Cow and the Sheep

A man owns a horse, a cow and a sheep. He also owns a pasture.

If the horse and cow can eat the contents of the pasture in 40 days, while the horse and sheep can do it in 60 days and the cow and the sheep in 90 days, how long all of them together will take to eat all the contents?

The Two Mathematical Men

In Bangalore there is a well known Science Institute. During a visit I asked two of the men to tell me their ages. One replied, 'One of our ages subtracted from the other's equals 30.'

Then the other man spoke, 'Our ages multiplied together equal 1624.'

What were their ages?

A Question of Mileage

If 5 tyres were used on a car which has travelled 20,000 miles, how many miles did each tyre sustain, if all the tyres were used equally in sustaining this mileage?

A Problem of Dissection

The shape shown in the sketch below, obviously, is that of a square attached to half of another similar square, divided diagonally:

Can you divide it into four pieces all of precisely the same size and shape?

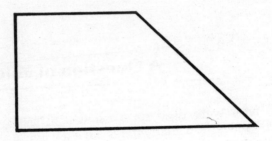

118
The Sixteen Fours

How can you make a total of 1,000 by using sixteen 4's?

119
The Strange Two Numbers

There are two whole numbers, difference of their squares is a cube and the difference of their cubes is a square. These are the smallest possible numbers.

Can you find the numbers?

120
How Much?

I have two 10 paise coins. If $4/5$ of what I have is $8/9$ of what you have, how much do you have?

121
The 'Mixed Double'

Four married couples played a tennis tournament of 'mixed doubles'. A man and a woman always played against a man and a woman. However, no person ever played with or against any other person more than once. They all played together in two courts on three successive days.

Can you show how they could have done it?

122
The Bargain

Sometimes one is mystified at the startling reductions some people make in their prices and wonders on what principle the reductions are based. To quote an example three years ago a friend offered me a used typewriter for Rs. 1024. A year later he offered me the same for Rs. 640 and last year he wanted Rs. 400 and now he is willing to sell it to me for Rs. 250. But I have decided to buy it when he reduces next time.

If he does a consistent reduction, at what price will he offer the typewriter to me next?

123
At the Fair

At the fair I bought 6 pineapples and two jackfruits for Rs. 15. If I could have bought 4 more pineapples for Rs. 14 than jackfruits for Rs. 9. What would be the price of each?

124
Sections of a Necklace

I have five sections of a necklace—each section consisting of four links. I took the sections to a goldsmith and asked him to give me an estimate to join the 5 sections into a one piece necklace. The goldsmith wanted Re.1 to cut open a link and Re. 1 to solder it together again.

What is the cheapest method and how much should it cost me to get the five pieces joined together into one full necklace?

125
The Problem of Square Boards

I have three square boards, the surface of the first containing five square feet more than the second, and the second containing five square feet more than the third.

Can you find the exact measurements for the sides of the boards?

126

Age of Demochares

This is an ancient problem dating back to about 310 A.D.

Demochares had lived one-fourth of his life as a boy, one-fifth as a youth, one-third as a man, and has spent thirteen years in his dotage. How old is Demochares?

127

The Age Old Problem

The combined ages of Reena and Seena are 44 years and Reena is twice as old as Seena was when Reena was half as old as Seena will be when Seena is three times as old as Reena was when Reena was three times as old as Seena.

How old is Reena?

128
The Painted Cube

A cubic object 3" × 3" × 3" is painted blue on all the outside surfaces, including the top and bottom. If the cube is cut into 27 cubes of 1" × 1" × 1", how many 1" cubes do have any painted surfaces?

129
Smoking Not Prohibited

A standard-sized cigarette can be rolled out of 6 standard-sized cigarette butts. How many cigarettes can be made and smoked from 36 butts?

130
Mathematical Taxi Driver

Some times small town taxi drivers can be very rude. One taxi driver I had the occasion to travel with was particularly lacking in courtesy, and so I asked for his number.

The driver gave me a sardonical smile and said, 'Well, if you divide my number by 2, 3, 4, 5 or 6 you will find there is always 1 remaining. But if you divide it by 11 there is no remainder. Do you want to know something more? There is no other cabby in this town with a lower number than—who can say the same,' and he drove off, while I stood there completely baffled.

What was the man's number?

131
The Tennis Tournament

A singles tennis tournament is held in which 30 men participate. If a player is eliminated as soon as he loses a match, how many matches are required to determine the winner?

Dividing the Load Equally

On my return to India, after an extensive tour of America, I waited for the two crates I had sent by ship as unaccompanied baggage.

When they finally arrived, I had them cleared through the Customs and engaged three labourers to carry them to my home 3 miles distant. I was going to pay them Rs. 8 each for this task.

As I was going to pay each of them equal amounts, they decided to carry a crate each equal distance.

How did they manage to do it?

Longfellow and His Bees

Here is a simple arithmetical puzzle set by Longfellow in his own flowery, poetical language.

If one-fifth of a hive of bees flew to the badamba flower, one-third flew to the slandbara, three times the difference of these two numbers flew to an arbour, and one bee continued to fly about, attracted on each side by the fragrant Ketaki and Malati, what was the total number of bees?

Mr. Portchester's Problem

Last time I saw Mr. Portchester in London he was facing a serious problem pouring his wine from one vessel to the other.

Mr. Portchester had two ten quart containers full of wine. He also had a five quart and a four quart measure.

All he wanted to do was put exactly three quarts into each of the two measures. He was standing there wondering how he should do it!

Now I offered to help and gave him some suggestions.

Can you find out what was my suggestion, and how many manipulations of pouring from one vessel to the other did he require, without waste of any wine, tilting or other tricks.

Driving Through the Country

I decided to drive through the country leisurely, and on the first day I did only 7 miles. On the last day I did 51 miles, increasing my journey 4 miles each day.

How many days did I travel and how far?

Dots and Lines

Nine dots are arranged by 3 rows of 3 in the form of a square as shown in the sketch below:

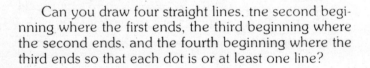

Can you draw four straight lines, the second beginning where the first ends, the third beginning where the second ends, and the fourth beginning where the third ends so that each dot is or at least one line?

The Triangles

How many triangles, of any size, are there in this star.

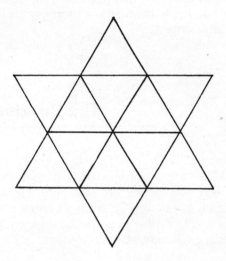

138
The Sabbath Day

Christians hold the first day of the week as Sabbath, the Jews the seventh, and the Turks the sixth.

How can these three, have their own true Sabbath on the same day?

139
The Puzzled Artist

An artist wanted to paint a picture on a canvas which would allow for a margin of 4 inches on top and bottom and two inches on each side. He wanted the picutre itself to occupy 72 square inches.

What would be the smallest dimensions, the canvas he is going to obtain, should possess?

140
The Mystery of Number Eleven

Can you find the largest possible number containing any 9 of the 10 digits, considering 0 also as a number, that is divisible by 11, without a remainder?

141
The Rose Garden

In my bungalow in Bangalore I have a beautiful rose garden.

The four sides of the garden are known to be 20, 16, 12 and 10 rods. And it is also known that it has the greatest possible area for those sides.

Can you find the area?

Squares Within Square

In the illustration below, how many squares are there?

143
The Farmer and the Animals

Farmer Thimmayya bought some mules at Rs. 50 each, sheep at Rs. 40 each, goats at Rs. 25 each, and pigs at Rs. 10 each. The average price of the animals per head worked to Rs. 30.

How many animals of each kind did he buy?

144
The House Where She Lives

It was at a cocktail party in New York that I met Stephanie. We exchanged our phone numbers and decided to meet each other soon.

When she rang up and invited me to her house this is how she gave me the number of her house:

'I live in a long street. Numbered on the side of my house are the houses one, two, three and so on. All the numbers on one side of my house add up to exactly the same as all the numbers on the other side of my house. I know there are more than fifty houses on that side of the street, but not so many as five hundred '

Can you find Stephanie's house number?

The Mango Thieves

One night three naughty boys stole a basketful of mangoes from a garden, hid the loot and went to sleep Before retiring they did some quick counting and found that the fruits were less than a hundred in number.

During the night one boy awoke, counted the mangoes and found that he could divide the mangoes into three equal parts if he first took one for himself He then took one mango, ate it up, and took $\frac{1}{3}$ of the rest, hid them separately and went back to sleep.

Shortly thereafter another boy awoke, counted the mangoes and he again found that if he took one for himself the loot could be divided into three equal parts. He ate up one mango, bagged $\frac{1}{3}$ of the remainder, hid them separately and went back to sleep. The third boy also awoke after some time, did the same and went back to sleep.

In the morning when they all woke up, and counted their mangoes, they found that the remaining mangoes again totalled 1 more than could be divided into three equal parts.

How many mangoes did the boys steal?

A Matter of Rupees and Paise

I have a money pouch containing Rs. 700. There are equal number of 25 paise coins, 50 paise coins and one rupee coins.

How many of each are there?

Sawing the Cube

We have a wooden cube of 3" on a side and we have a buzz-saw. The cube can be cut into 27 one inch cubes by the buzz-saw. Only 6 cuts of saw are necessary to do this, while keeping the pieces together. Now, can you reduce the number of cuts by rearranging the pieces after each cut? If you can, how is it done? If you can't, why can't it be done?

148
The Two Trains

Two trains start at the same time, one from Bangalore to Mysore and the other from Mysore to Bangalore. If they arrive at their destinations one hour and four hours respectively after passing one another, how much faster is one train running than the other?

149
The Squares

Can you find four numbers such that the sum of every two and the sum of all four may be perfect squares?

150
The Arithmetical Landlady

While house hunting in London, I came across a very good leasehold property. Discussing the lease the landlady told me:

'The property was originally on a 99 years lease and two-thirds of the time passed is equal to four-fifths of the time to come. Now work it out for yourself and see how many years are there to go!'

Solutions

1

The first brother is 70 inches tall, the second 72, the third 74 and the fourth brother 80 inches tall.

2

Twenty-six minutes.

3

Since the boys have as many brothers as sisters, there must be 1 boy more than the number of girls. If we try 2 and 1, 3 and 2, and 4 and 3, we will find that 4 boys and 3 girls is the solution to fulfil the requirement that each girl has twice as many brothers as sisters.

4

Naturally, the train travelling against the spin of the earth. This train will wear out its wheels more quickly, because the centrifugal force is less on this train.

5

No, the answer is not $32^1/_2$ miles an hour, though this figure is the obvious answer! However, this represents the average of the 2 speeds and not the average speed for the whole trip.

If the time is equal to the distance divided by the average speed, then the time for the trip starting from San Francisco equals $S/_{40}$ and the time for the return trip is $S/25$ which gives us a total time of $S/40 + S/25$, which equals $13S/200$.

Therefore, the average speed for the whole trip when the average speed equals the distance divided by the time is 2S divided by $13S/200$ which equals 2S times $200/13S$, which equals $400S/13S$ or $30 - 10/13$ miles an hour.

6

The lowest square number I can think of, containing all the nine digits once and only once, is 139854276, the square of 11826, and the highest square number under the same conditions is 923187456 the square of 30384.

7

One can think of different answers for this question, but yet the correct answer is very simple. All we have to consider is that the shop owner could not have possibly lost more than the tourist actually stole.

The tourist got away with the bicycle which cost the shop owner Rs. 300 and the Rs. 50 'change', and therefore, he made off with Rs. 350. And this is the exact amount of the shopkeeper's loss.

8

By experiment we find that the only numbers that can be turned upside down and still read as a number are 0, 1, 6, 8 and 9.

The numbers, 0, 1 and 8 remain 0, 1 and 8 when turned over, but 6 becomes 9 and 9 becomes 6. Therefore, the possible numbers on the bus were 9, 16, 81, 100, 169 or 196. However, the number 196 is the only number which becomes a perfect square when turned over because 961 is the perfect square of 31.

Therefore, 196 is the correct answer.

9

Here is the formula that gives the minutes past twelve to which the hour hand points when the minute hand is exactly thirty minutes ahead.

Minutes past twelve $Y = \frac{30}{11} [(n-1) 2+1]$

where n is the next hour—

Let's take the case of at what time between 4 and 5 will the hands be opposite each other? (n=5).

$\therefore Y = \frac{3}{11} \times 9 = \frac{270}{11} + 24\frac{6}{11}$.

i.e. the hour hand will be $24\frac{6}{11}$ minutes past 4.

The formula may be derived from the following:

If X is distance moved by the minute hand

Y is the distance moved by hour hand

then X−Y = 30

First time the hands move round X = 12 Y

Second time the hands move round X = 12 Y−5

Third time the hands move round X = 12 Y−10 etc.

10

The Police Officer took thirty steps. In the same time the thief took forty-eight, which added to his start o

twenty-seven, that means he took seventy-five steps.
This distance would be exactly equal to thirty steps of
the Police Officer.

11

While striking 7 the clock strikes its first gong at 7
o'clock and it strikes 6 more at regular intervals. These
6 intervals take 7 seconds so that the intervals between
gongs is $^7/_6$ seconds. However, to strike 10 there are
9 intervals each taking $^7/_6$ seconds for a total of $10^1/_2$
seconds.

12

In order that the little girl should have disposed of the
oranges she had remaining after her second sale, she
must have had at least one whole orange remaining so
that she could deduct from it 'half of her oranges plus
half an orange', for the third and the final sale. Therefore, if 1 orange represents half of the remaining after
the second sale, then she must have sold two oranges
in her second sale, leaving the 3 oranges after the first
sale.

Lastly, if three oranges only represent half the original number, plus half an orange , then she must have
started with $[(3 \times 2) + 1]$ or 7 oranges.

13

All the transactions carried out through the counterfeit
note are invalid, and, therefore, everybody stands in

relation to his debtor just where he was before I picked up the note.

14

A pound of cotton is heavier than a pound of gold because cotton is weighed by the avoirdupois pound, which consists of 16 ounces, whereas gold, being a precious metal is weighed by the troy pound which contains 12 ounces (5760 grams).

15

When Tinku takes 12, Rinku and Jojo will take 9 and 14, respectively—and then they would have taken altogether thirty-five nuts.

Thirty-five is contained in 770 twenty-two times which means all one has to do now is merely multiply 12, 9 and 14 by 22 to find that Tinku's share was 264, Rinku's 198 and Jojo's 308.

Now as the total of their ages is $17^1/2$ years or half the sum of 12, 9 and 14, their respective ages must be 6, $4^1/2$ and 7 years.

16

Jayant was 24 and Mohini 18.

17

The minimum number of weights required is five and these should weigh 1, 3, 9, 27 and 81 pounds.

18

Let's assume G is the number of glasses delivered intact. Then,

$3G$ = the amount earned.

Let's assume B is the number of glasses broken. Then,

$9B$ = the amount forfeited

$3G - 9B = 240$

$9B = -240$

$G + B = 100$

$3B = 300$

$\overline{128 = 60}$

$\therefore \quad B = 5$ and $G = 95$

19

The number is 27, 2 + 7 = 9, $\qquad 9 \times 3 = 27$

20

$81\frac{5643}{297}$ $\qquad$ $81\frac{7524}{396}$ $\qquad$ $82\frac{3546}{197}$

$91\frac{5742}{638}$ $\qquad$ $91\frac{5823}{647}$ $\qquad$ $91\frac{7524}{836}$

$94\frac{1578}{263}$ $\qquad$ $96\frac{1428}{357}$ $\qquad$ $96\frac{1752}{438}$

$\qquad\qquad$ $96\frac{2148}{537}$ and $\qquad$ $3\frac{69258}{714}$

21

I don't know about you, but I would have handed over 5 two paise stamps, 30 one paisa stamps and 7 five paise stamps.

22

There isn't really any mystery, because the explanation is simple. While the two ways of selling are only identical, when the number of marbles sold at three for a paisa and two for a paisa is in the proportion of three to two. Therefore, if the first woman had handed over 36 marbles and the second woman 24, they would have fetched 24 paise, immaterial of, whether sold separately or at five for 2 paise. But if they had the same number of marbles which led to loss of 1 paisa when sold together, in every 60 marbles. So, if they had 60 each, there would be a loss of 2 paise and if there were 90 each (180 altogether) they would lose 3 paise and so on.

In the case of 60, the missing 1 paisa arises from the fact that the 3 marbles per paisa woman gains 2 paise and the 2 marbles per paisa woman loses 3 paise.

The first woman receives $9^1/_2$ paise and the second woman $14^1/_2$, so that each loses $^1/_2$ paise in the transaction.

23

The couple arrived home 10 minutes earlier than usual. Therefore, the point at which they met must have been 5 minutes driving time from the station. Thus, the wife should have been at that point at five minutes to six. Since the man started to walk at five o'clock, he must have been walking for 55 minutes when he met his wife.

24

At each station passengers can get tickets for any of the other 24 stations and, therefore, the number of tickets required is $25 \times 24 = 600$.

25

My aunt's share was Rs. $49200 \frac{10}{13}$

26

We can build concentric hexagons containing 1, 6, 12, 18, 24, 30, 36 and 42 circles. When R/r becomes sufficiently large there will be room for extra circles.

If there is an even number of circles per side in last hexagon, an outsider can be placed centrally, if

$$\frac{R}{r} \geq \frac{1 + \sqrt{\frac{3}{2}}}{1 - \sqrt{\frac{3}{2}}} \quad \text{i.e. if } \frac{R}{r} \geq 13.9.$$

Two more 'outsiders' can be put each side of this one, if

$$[(R+r)^2 \left(\sqrt{\frac{3}{2}} \right)^2 + (2r)^2] + r \leq R$$

i.e. if $0 \leq \frac{R^2}{r^2} - 14 \frac{R}{r} - 15$

i.e. if $0 \leqslant \left(\dfrac{R}{r} + 1 \right) \left(\dfrac{R}{r} - 1 \right)$

i.e. if $\dfrac{R}{r} \geqslant 15$.

Therefore, in the given example three outsiders can be accommodated.

And the number of saucers that can be placed on the table are:

$1 + 6 + 12 + 18 + 24 + 30 + 36 + 42 + (3 \times 6) = 187$

27

If I walk 26 steps I require 30 seconds.

If I walk 34 steps I require only 18 seconds.

Multiplying 30 by 34 and 26 by 18 we get 1020 and 468.

The difference between 1020 and 468 is 552.

When we divide this number by the difference between 30 and 18, i.e. by 12 we get the answer 46—the number of steps in the stairway.

28

No It cannot be done.

Each rectangle covers one white square and one black square, because on a chess board the white and black squares are always adjacent.

The two squares which we remove from the chess board are of the same colour, and so the remaining board has two more boxes of one colour than the other. And after the rectangles have covered 60 boxes, there will be left two squares of the same colour.

Obviously the remaining rectangle cannot cover these two squares.

29

Just one look at the number 999919 and we know that it cannot be a prime number. And if the problem has to have only one answer, this number can have only two factors. The factors are 991 and 1009, both of which are primes.

We know that each cat killed more mice than there were cats, and, therefore, the correct answer, clearly, is that 991 cats killed 1009 mice.

30

The forewheel is 8 feet in circumference and the hind wheel 12 feet.

31

If X is the temperature $\frac{9X}{5} = X - 32$

i.e. $\frac{4X}{5} = -32$

which gives X = −40

i.e. −40°C = −40°F.

32

The entire mile was run in nine minutes. Though from the facts given we cannot determine the time taken over the first and second quarter-miles separately, we know, however, that together they took four and a half minutes. And the last two quarters were run in two and a quarter minutes each.

33
The clock broken in the manner shown in the illustration below:

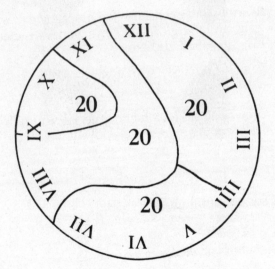

The numerals on each of the four parts will sum to 20.

34

The painted area as shown in the illustration below:

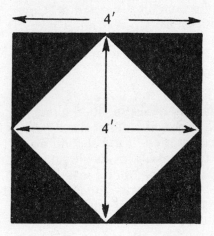

Though it does not leave the clear area $4' \times 4'$, however, does measure $4'$ from top to bottom and from side to side.

35

We know that there were five droves with an equal number in each drove, and, therefore, the number must be divisible by 5. As every one of the eight dealers bought the same number of animals, the number must also be divisible by 8. This leads us to the conclusion that the number must be a multiple of 40.

Now the highest possible multiple of 40 that will work is 120, and this number could be made up in one of two ways—1 cow, 23 sheep and 96 pigs or 3 cows. 8 sheep and 109 pigs. But the first does not fit in because the animals consisted of 'Cows, Sheep and Pigs' and a single 'Cow' is not 'Cows'. Therefore, the second possibility is the correct answer.

36

$8/7$th of Rs. 35 equals Rs. 40, the regular selling price of the first frock and $7/6$th of Rs. 30 equals Rs. 35, the regular selling price of the second frock. Now, if the first frock usually sells for Rs. 40 and is sold for Rs. 35 on the reduced price, then I save Rs. 5. This gives me a gain on the cost the percentage of $5/35$ which equals $1/7$ and that is a little more than 14.28.

The second frock usually sells for Rs. 35, which on the reduced price costs me Rs. 30. Again I save Rs. 5 which equals $5/30$ or $1/6$ that amounts to, in percentage, a gain of little more than 16.66. The difference between the first frock and the second in terms of percentage gained is a little more than 2.38. Hence, the second frock is a better buy.

37

The key to the solution is that with a little bit of pencil work, it will be found, while I can walk 5 miles, my friend who started from Tumkur can walk 7 miles. Let's assume the distance between Bangalore and Tumkur is 24 miles, then the point of meeting would be 14 miles from Bangalore, and, therefore, I walked $3^3/7$ miles per hour while my friend walked $4^4/5$ miles per hour, and we both arrived exactly at 7 P.M.

38

Let's assume that the man and the train normally meet at the crossing at 8 A.M., then the usual time of the cyclist at the bend is 8 A.M. and he is 6 miles behind at 7.30 A.M. But when the cyclist is late, he arrives at the bend at 8.25 A.M. and therefore he is six miles behind at 7.55 A.M. Since the train takes 5 minutes to travel the six mile run, the speed of the train is 72 m.p.h.

39

The woman made altogether Rs. 20. She made Rs. 10 when she sold the item for the first time and another Rs. 10 when she sold it for the second time.

40

The number is 84.

41

The manufacturer must take one flywheel made by each machine, find their total weight and compare this with the weight of the equivalent number of good flywheels to obtain the difference. Then, he must take 1 flywheel from machine number one, 2 flywheels from machine number two and so forth, and weigh these against the correct weight for that number of parts.

42

While the first was the example given, the top row must be one of the four following numbers: 192. 219. 273 or 327.

43

44

The merchant must mix 70 Kilos of the Rs. 32 coffee with 30 Kilos of Rs. 40 coffee.

45
I must have had Rs. 42 in my purse when I started!

46
4, 5 and 6.

47
If the sari cost Rs. 100 and the blouse Rs. 10 the difference would be Rs. 90, and therefore, the sari must cost more and the blouse less. A little thought indicates the sari costs Rs. 105 and the blouse Rs. 5. So, the difference in cost is Rs. 100.

48
The date on which I met the boy was 1st January 1977, and the boy's birthday was on 31st December, 1965 The boy was 11 years old on the day I met him.

49
The whole block weighs 3 lbs.

50
They had Rs. 22781.25.

51

Let's assume that the age of the ship at present is X years and of the boiler Y years.

Then

The ship X is twice as old as its boiler (Y – X) was when the ship was (x-X) as old as the boiler is now.

∴ X = 2 (Y – X) and (x – X) = 2.
Eliminating X gives 4Y = 3x.
Also, x + Y = 30

∴ Y (the boiler) = $\frac{90}{7}$ years.
and X (the ship)

$$= \frac{120}{7} \text{ years.}$$

52

The following would be the procedure in chart form:

	19 Ounces	13 Ounces	7 Ounces
	0	13	7
Step 1	7	13	0
Step 2	19	1	0
Step 3	12	1	7
Step 4	12	8	0
Step 5	5	8	7
Step 6	5	13	2
Step 7	18	0	2
Step 8	18	2	0
Step 9	11	2	7
Step 10	11	9	0
Step 11	4	9	7
Step 12	4	13	3
Step 13	17	0	3

	19 Ounces	13 Ounces	7 Ounces
Step 14	17	3	0
Step 15	10	3	7

53

Just myself! Only I was going to the market and I met all the others coming from the opposite direction.

54

The fraction is $\frac{7}{13}$

55

They will never step out with right foot together.

56

Mammu should take out 3 socks from the drawer because if she takes out only 2 then, both could be of different colours However the third selection would result in a pair of white or brown socks.

57

As Rekha's share falls in through her death, the farm has now to be divided only between Rashmi and Mala. in the proportion of one-third to one-fourth—that is in the proportion of four-twelfths to three. Therefore, Rashmi gets four-sevenths of the hundred acres and Mala three-sevenths.

58

Ten applicants had neither mathematics nor literature training. So, we can now concentrate on the remaining 90 applicants. Of the 90, twenty had got no mathematics **training** and eight had got no literary training.

That leaves us with a remainder of 62 who have had training in both literature and mathematics.

59

The man must have lost. And the longer he went on the more he would lose—with simple calculations. we can draw this conclusion:

In two tosses he was left with three quarters of his money.

In six tosses with twenty-seven sixty-fourths of his money, and so on.

Immaterial of the order of the wins and losses. he loses money. so long as their number is in the end equal.

60

28 is the answer.

The method of working out this problem is to reverse the whole process—multiplying 2 by 10, deducting 8. squaring the result and so on.

61

$$\sqrt{40^2 + 9^2} \text{ ft} = \sqrt{1600 + 81} \text{ ft} = \sqrt{1681} \text{ ft} = 41 \text{ feet}.$$

62

There were sixty eyes, so there must have been thirty animals. Now the question is what combination of four-legged pigs and two-legged ducks adding to.thirty will give 86 feet. With some pencil work, we get the answer 13 pigs and 17 ducks.

63

If 65 minutes be counted on the face of the same watch then the problem would be impossible, because the hands must coincide every $65^5/11$ minutes as shown by its face—and it hardly matters whether it runs fast or slow. However, if it is measured by actual time, it gains $^5/11$ of a minute in 65 minutes or $^{60}/_{148}$ of a minute per hour.

64

The simplest way is to find those numbers between 50 and 100, which are multiples of 2 and 3 leaving no remainder. These numbers are 54, 60, 66, 72, 78, 84, 90 and 96. By scrutiny we find that if 78 is divided by 5 it will give 15 plus 3 left over. Therefore, 78 is the total number of eggs Rasool had in his basket, before the accident. And, therefore, he was paid Rs. 39 by the gentleman.

65

The value per sheep was Rs. 30.

66

The trains travel at 25 miles per hour. Therefore, they will meet after travelling for one hour and the falcon also must have been flying for one hour. Since it travels at 100 miles per hour, the bird must have flown 100 miles.

67

At a raise of Rs. 300 per year:
Ist year Rs. 1000   + Rs. 1000 = Rs. 2000
2nd year Rs. 1150 + Rs. 1150 = Rs. 2300
3rd year Rs. 1300 + Rs. 1300 = Rs. 2600
4th year Rs. 1450 + Rs. 1450 = Rs. 2900

At a raise of Rs. 100 each half year:
Ist year Rs. 1000   + Rs. 1100 = Rs. 2100
2nd year Rs. 1200 + Rs. 1300 = Rs. 2500
3rd year Rs. 1400 + Rs. 1500 = Rs. 2900
4th year Rs. 1600 + Rs. 1700 = Rs. 3300

Obviously the second proposition is much more lucrative.

68

Mammu had 5 marbles and Nawal 7

69

The ages must be as follows:
Mrs. Sareen   39
Sudha   21
Seema   18

Reema	18
Sonny	12
Kishu	9

It is obvious that Seema and Reema are twins.

70

Since 437 contains the percentage of all apartments including the number of 4's and total of these percentage is 244, the number of 4's must be represented by 100% as the base. In order to find the base of 100% representing the number of 4's, we have to divide 437 by 244%, which gives us 179.0984. Thus, we can work out a table showing the number of each type apartment, which should look as follows:

Type of Apartment	Number of Apartments	Rounded out to the nearest figure
2	8.9549	9
$2\frac{1}{2}$'s	12.5369	13
3's	26.8647	27
$3\frac{1}{2}$'s	35.8197	36
4's	179.0984	179
$4\frac{1}{2}$'s	87.7582	88
5's	59.1024	59
$5\frac{1}{2}$'s	21.4918	21
6's	5.3729	5
Total	436.9799	437

71

There are only 5 numbers that can be read upside down — 0, 1, 6, 8 and 9. Now we only have to arrange these numbers so that when turned upside down the result will be larger by 78633. With some experiment we will find that the number is 10968 which is 89601, inverted.

72

He sold one for Rs. 600 losing 20% on the transaction. So, he must have paid Rs. 750 for that lathe and since he made 20% profit on the other machine he must have bought it for Rs. 500. Therefore, his total loss is of Rs. 50.

73

In the first three pickings you may get 1 of each colour, on the 4th pick there will be at least two of one colour.

Therefore, the answer is 4.

74

A brick weighed 3 lbs. Therefore, 16 bricks weighed 48 lbs and 11 bricks 33 lbs. Multiplying 48 by 33 and taking the square root we get 39.79. The girl's weight must have been about 39.79 lbs.

75

As the difference between twice the number and half

of it amounts to 45. or half of the number plus the whole of its represented by 1 adds up to 45.

$$\frac{1}{2} + 1 = \frac{1}{2} + \frac{2}{2} = \frac{3}{2} = 45$$

Now we have to find what number $3/2$ is equal of 45. To do this we invert $3/2$ to $2/3$ and multiply by 45. This gives us

$$\frac{2}{3} \times 45 = 30$$

Therefore, 30 is the number.

76

Eleven minutes. The twelfth piece does not require sawing.

77

The train schedule must have been in the following manner:

Churchgate train into the station at	1.00 P.M.
And Bandra train at	1.01 P.M.
Churchgate train into the station at	1.10 P.M.
And Bandra train at	1.11 P.M.
Churchgate train into the station at	1.20 P.M.
And Bandra train at	1.21 P.M.

and so on and so forth.

This way each train would be arriving every ten minutes but his chances of getting the Churchgate train would be 9 times as great as of getting the Bandra train, because if he arrives in the station between 1.20 P.M. and 1.21 P.M. he goes on the Bandra train but if he arrives between 1.21 P.M. and 1.30 P.M. he goes to Churchgate.

78

14 and 20.

79

The writers spent Rs. 350, the doctors also spent Rs. 350, the dentists spent Rs. 420 and the bank employees spent Rs. 210. Thus, they spent altogether Rs. 1330. The five writers spent as much as four doctors, twelve doctors spent as much as nine dentists, and six dentists as much as eight bank employees.

80

I must have entered the store with Rs. 99.98 in my purse.

81

Let's assume P is a coin that's known to be imperfect. The solution to this problem runs as follows:

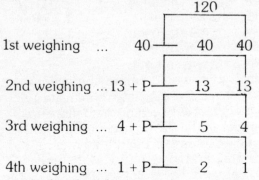

1st weighing   ...   40 —— 40   40

2nd weighing ... 13 + P —— 13   13

3rd weighing ...   4 + P —— 5   4

4th weighing ...   1 + P —— 2   1

And in the fifth and the last weighing we determine the actual faulty coin.

82

The container would be half full on the 9th day. Since the number of bacteria doubles each day, the container should be half full on the day before it became full.

83

The number is 120.

84

A simple general solution to this problem would be as follows:

Let's assume there are n number of players. Then the amount held by every player at the end will be $m(2^n)$, and the last winner must have held at the start $m(n+1)$, the next $m(2n+1)$, the next $m(4n+1)$ and so on to the first player, who must have held $m(2^{n-1}n+1)$.

Therefore, in this case, $n = 7$

And the amount held by every player at the end was 2^7 quarter of a rupee pieces.

Therefore, $m = 1$

Govind started with 8 quarter of a rupee pieces or
Rs. 2.

Fakhruddin started with 15 quarter of a rupee
pieces or Rs. 3.75.

Edward started with 29 quarter of a rupee pieces
or Rs. 7.25.

Dev started with 57 quarter of a rupee pieces
or Rs. 14.25.

Chunder started with 113 quarter of a rupee pieces
or Rs. 28.25

Binoy started with 225 quarter of a rupee pieces
or Rs. 56.25.
Arun started with 449 quarter of a rupee pieces
or Rs. 112.25.

85

Ram Rakhan worked for $16^2/3$ days and idled $13^1/3$ days.

His salary at Rs. 240 per 30 day month works out to Rs. 8 a day. At Rs. 8 a day, working $16^2/3$ days he earned Rs. 133.33 and idling $13^1/3$ days he lost also Rs. 133.33. Therefore neither owed the other anything.

86

The person who moves when there are 5 matchsticks will lose the game, because if you remove one matchstick the other person will take the remaining 4, and if that person takes two then you will take the remaining 3, so on and so forth. Therefore, the person who moves when there are 10 or 15 matchsticks will lose.

The only correct way to make the first move is to take away 2 matchsticks and reduce the pile to 15, then no matter what your opponent does on his move, you reduce the pile to 10, then to 5 and lastly you take the remaining matchsticks.

87

First I was offered 16 guavas for Rs. 1.20. That would

have been at the rate of 90 paise a dozen. The two extra guavas gave me 18 for Rs. 1.20, which is at the rate of eighty paise a dozen, which amounts to en paise a dozen less than the original price settled.

88

Shepherd Gopal had one sheep only.

89

The ratio of the father and son's age is now 4 to 1, and 30 years from now it will be 2 to 1. The period of thirty years equals the difference of the two ratios or 2 to 1 Therefore, $30 \times 2 = 60$, the father's age and $^1/_2 \times 30 = 15$, the son's age.

90

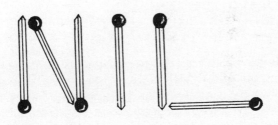

91

I had one 50 paise coin, one 25 paise coin and four 10 paise coins.

92

Let's consider the year 1948. Fortyeight has the following factors:

24 and	2	i.e.	24th of February
4 and	12	i.e.	4th of December
12 and	4	i.e.	12th of April
16 and	3	i.e.	16th of March
6 and	8	i.e.	6th of August or
8 and	6	i.e.	8th of June

and giving six dates. The years 36, 48, 60 and 72 each give six dates whereas the maximum number of such dates is given by the year 24—seven occasions.

93

The bucket full of half sovereign gold pieces are worth more since the denominations of the gold pieces make no difference. What is most important here is the bucket containing half sovereign gold pieces is full of gold whereas the other one is only half full.

94

Double the product of the two distances from the wall and you get 144, which is the square of 12. The sum of the two distances is 17, and when we add these two numbers, 12 and 17 together and also subtract one from the other, we get two answers 29 and 5 as the radius, or half-diameter of the table. Naturally the diameter should be 58" or 10". However, a table of the latter dimensions cannot be a 'large circular table' and therefore, the table must be 58" in diameter.

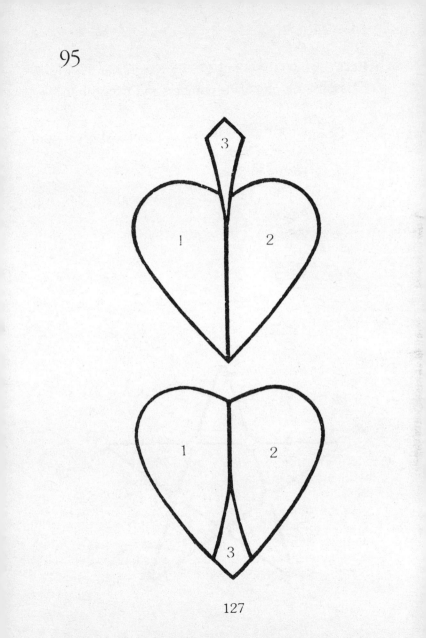

Let's assume X is one of the numbers and Y the other.
Then,

$$X^2 - Y^2 = 51 \text{ (i)}$$
$$X - Y = 3 \text{ (ii)}$$
Divide (i) & (ii)
$$X + Y = 17 \text{ (iii)}$$
Add (ii) & (iii)
$$2X = 20$$
$$X = 10$$
$$Y = 7$$

97

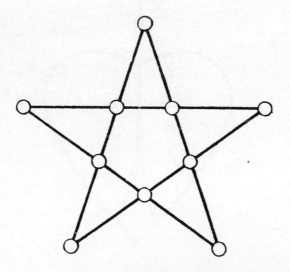

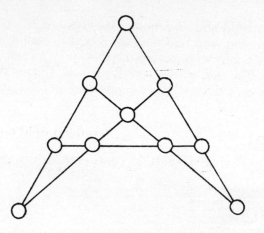

98
Since the squirrel climbs 5 ft. in ascending 4 ft. of the pole, he travels 20 ft. in climbing 16 ft.

99
The man's rate of speed is 4 miles an hour to the woman's 3 miles and,therefore,their total rate is 7 miles an hour. Since they are 63 miles apart they can cover an average of 9 miles in one hour. Therefore, $9 \times 4 = 36$ miles travelled by the man and $9 \times 3 = 27$ miles the distance travelled by the woman.

100
The three men shared the beer equally and so each drank the contents of $2^2/3$ bottles. Therefore, the mar

who had bought 5 bottles contributed $2^1/3$ bottles and the man who had paid for 3 bottles contributed $^1/3$ of the bottle. to make up the third man's share.

The first man's contribution is 7 times that of the second and,therefore,he gets Rs. 7 and the latter Re. 1.

101

The woman's age is 45 years and her husband's 54.

102

When the trains are moving in opposite directions, they are passing each other with the combined speeds of the two trains. Hence, when going in the same direction, the 'passing speed' is the speed of the passenger speed minus the speed of the goods train.

If the passenger train goes twice as fast as the goods train, then the passing speed when going in the opposite directions will be 2 plus 1 or 3 compared with 2 minus 1 or 1 when the trains are going in the same direction.

Therefore. the answer is twice as fast.

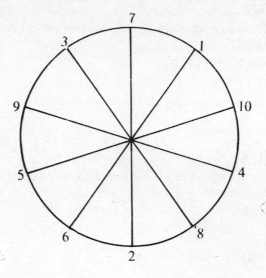

104
One of the answers is that there were 5 old persons, 25 young persons and 70 children.

105
$3^3 + 3 + {}^3/_3$.

106
There were 72 bees.

107

12 cows grazing once = 24 cows grazing twice
9 Mules = 13 $\frac{1}{2}$ cows
Divide 500 in ratio
24 : 13 $\frac{1}{2}$
First man paid Rs. 180 and second man Rs. 320.

108

The candles must have burnt for three hours and three quarters as one candle had one-sixteenth of its total length left and the other four-sixteenths.

109

200 feet.

110

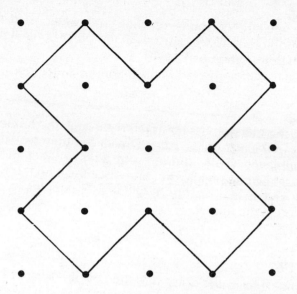

111

The crew can row $1/5$ of the distance per minute on still water and the stream does half that distance per minute

The difference and sum of these two fractions are $7/60$ and $17/60$. Hence, rowing against the stream would take $60/17$ minutes and with the stream $60/17$ minutes.

The correct answer is $3\,9/17$ minutes.

112

The mixture of spirits of wine and water is in the proportion of 40 to 1, just as in the other bottle it was in the proportion of 1 to 40.

113

For the train to pass completely through the tunnel, it has to travel 2 miles. After 1 mile, the train would be completely in the tunnel, and after another mile it would be completely out, and since the train is travelling at 1 mile a minute, it will take 2 minutes to pass through the tunnel.

114

Since it takes the horse and the cow 40 days, in 1 day $1/40$ of the pasture would be eaten, since it takes the horse and the sheep 60 days, in 1 day $1/60$ would be grazed, since it takes the cow and the sheep 90 days, in 1 day $1/90$ of the pasture would be devoured.

$$\frac{1}{40} + \frac{1}{60} + \frac{1}{90} = \frac{19}{360}$$

$19/360$ equals what 2 horses, 2 cows and 2 sheep eat in a day and

$$\frac{19}{360} \div 2 = \frac{19}{720}$$

$19/720$ equals what 1 horse, 1 cow and 1 sheep eat in 1 day.

As it takes to eat $1/720$ of the contents of the pasture $1/720$ will require 19th part of 1 day or $720/720$ or the whole of the contents of the pasture will require 720 times as many days.

$$\text{or } 37 - \frac{17}{19}$$
$$\therefore 19 : 1 :: 720 : 37 - \frac{17}{19}$$

115

Their ages were respectively 58 and 28.

116

When the car travels one mile each of 4 tyres sustain one mile's use.

Therefore, when a car has travelled 20,000 miles, a total of 80,000 tire miles has been used.

Since this mileage has been gathered on 5 tires, each tire must have been used for 16,000 miles.

117

Divide the figure up into 12 equal triangles, as shown

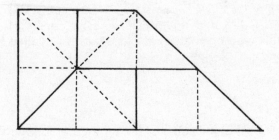

in the sketch and follow the direction of the cuts as indicated by the heavy lines.

118

$444 + 444 + 44 + 44 + 4 + 4 + 4 + 4 + 4 + 4$

119

$10^2 - 6^2 = 100 - 36 = 64 = 4^3$

$10^3 - 6^3 = 1000 - 216 = 784 = 28^2$

120

18 Paise.

121

Let's call the men A B C D and their wives E F G H. They must play in such a way that no person ever plays twice with or against another person.

	First Court	Second Court
1st day	AD against BF	CE against DF
2nd day	AH against CF	DE against BH
3rd day	AF against DG	BE against CH

In this way no man ever plays with or against his own wife.

122

It is obvious that the seller of the typewriter follows the rule to reduce three-eighths of the price at every reduction, and, therefore, after the consistent reduction, the typewriter should be next offered for Rs. 156.25.

123

Pineapples cost Rs. 1.75 a piece and jackfruits Rs. 2.25.

124

There is only one cheapest method and that is to open the 4 links of one section and then use these links to join the other 4 sections together, which should cost altogether Rs. 8.

125

The sides of the three boards measure 31 inches, 41 inches and 49 inches.

126

Demochares must be sixty years of age.

127

The ratio of Reena's age to Seena's must be as 5 to 3.

Since the sum of their age is 44, Reena must be $27^1/_2$ and Seena $16^1/_2$.

128

Only the box in the very centre of the stack will not

suffer the strokes of the paint brush, whereas all the other 26 boxes will have at least one side painted.

129

No, 6 is not the answer! It is not correct, because after the 6 cigarettes have been smoked there will again be 6 butts which can be made into another cigarette. The answer is 7

130

The driver's number was 121.

131

Every time a match is held, one player is eliminated and to eliminate 29 of the 30 players, 29 matches are required.

132

The first and the second labourers should each take a crate with the former carrying his load one mile and turning it over to the third, who will carry it two miles. Then the second labourer should carry his crate two miles and turn it over to the first, who will then carry it one mile. Thus, each carries a crate 2 miles.

133

The number of bees was 15

134

The following solution in eleven manipulations shows the contents of every vessel at the start and after every manipulation:

10 Quart	10 Quart	5 Quart	5 Quart
10	10	0	0
5	10	5	0
5	10	1	4
9	10	1	0
9	6	1	4
9	7	0	4
9	7	4	0
9	3	4	4
9	3	5	3
9	8	0	3
4	8	5	3
4	10	3	3

135

348 miles in 12 days.

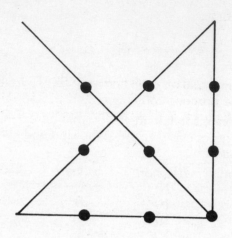

137
20 triangles.

138
From the Jews abode the Christian and the Turk set out on a tour round the world, the Christian going due east and the Turk due west. This way the Christian gains a day and the Turk loses a day. So that when they meet **again** at the house of the Jew their reckoning will agree with his and all three may keep their Sabbath on the same day.

139
The canvas must be 10 inches in width and 20 inches

in height and the picture itself 6 inches wide and 12 inches high.

140

With some trial one will find 987652413 as the highest possible number containing 9 of the 10 digits that is divisible by 11, without a remainder.

141

Half the sum of the side is 29 and from this we deduct the sides in turn, which gives us 9, 13, 17, 19, which when multiplied together make 37791. The square root of this number is 194.4.

194.4 square rods will be the answer.

142

30 squares.

143

He bought at least 1 mule, 1 ox, 2 goats and 1 pig.
Other answers are possible.

144

The numbers of the houses on each side will add up alike if the number of the house be 1 and there are no other houses, and if the number be 6 with 8 houses in all, if 35 with 49 houses, if 204 with 288 houses, if 1189 with 1681 houses and so on. But we know that there are more than 50 and less than 500 houses, and so we are limited to a single case.

The number of the house must be 204.

145

Assuming only 4 mangoes remained in the morning, this would mean that the third boy must have found 7 mangoes left when he woke up during night. But 7 is not $2/3$ of a whole number, so this is impossible.

The next possibility is 7 mangoes left in the morning, which is again impossible.

Now the next possibity is 10, which is $2/3$ of 15. This means that the third boy found 16 mangoes, took one and then took 5 more. The second boy then must have found 25 mangoes, taken one and then taken 8 more. But 25 is not $2/3$ of a whole number and, therefore, the assumption that 10 mangoes remained in the morning is absurd.

By similar reasoning the numbers 13, 16 and 19 can be eliminated, but 22 will be found to meet the required conditions.

The third boy found 34, took one and left $2/3$ of 33 or 22, the second boy found 52, took one and left $2/3$ of 51 or 34, the first boy found 79 took 1 and left $2/3$ of 78 or 52.

The answer is the boys stole altogether 79 mangoes.

146

25 paise + 50 paise + 100 paise = 175 paise and
Rs. 700 = 70,000 paise

$$\frac{70,000}{175} = 400$$

400 is the number for each denomination.

147

It cannot be done in less than six cuts, because the cube which is formed in the middle of the original cube has no exposed surface.

Since a cube has 6 sides, the saw must create this cube by 6 passes of the saw, no matter how the slices are rearranged.

148

One train was running just twice as fast as the other.

149

Besides several other answers, the smallest numbers that satisfies the conditions are:

a = 10430, b = 3970, c = 2114, d = 386
a + b = 10430 + 3970 = 14400 = 120^2
a + c = 10430 + 2114 = 12544 = 112^2
a + d = 10430 + 386 = 10816 = 104^2
b + c = 3970 + 2114 = 6084 = 78^2
b + d = 3970 + 386 = 4356 = 66^2
c + d = 2114 + 386 = 2500 = 50^2

$$a + b + c + d = 10430 + 3970 + 2114 + 386$$
$$= 16900 = 130^2$$

150
45 years.